To the staff and pupils of Bursar School, Cleethorpes
A.H.B.

Oxford University Press, Walton Street, Oxford OX2 6DP

Oxford New York
Athens Auckland Bangkok Bombay
Calcutta Cape Town Dar es Salaam Delhi
Florence Hong Kong Istanbul Karachi
Kuala Lumpur Madras Madrid Melbourne
Mexico City Nairobi Paris Singapore
Taipei Tokyo Toronto

and associated companies in
Berlin Ibadan

Oxford is a trade mark of Oxford University Press

A CIP catalogue record for this book is available
from the British Library

ISBN 0 19 279857 X (hardback)
ISBN 0 19 272298 0 (paperback)

Typeset by Pentacor PLC, High Wycombe, Bucks
Printed in Hong Kong

What's up the Coconut Tree?

A. H. Benjamin
Illustrated by Val Biro

Oxford University Press

Somewhere in the jungle was a coconut tree.
On its trunk was a notice.
It said: 'DON'T JUMP UP AND DOWN!'

Ostrich came and saw it.

DON'T
JUMP
UP AND
DOWN!

'Humph,' he said. 'I'll jump up and down
if I like.' And he did.

Bump! A coconut fell on his head.
'Ouch!' cried Ostrich. 'There must be something
up the coconut tree. I'll go and tell the king!'
And off he sprinted.

Nearby, on a small hill,
was another coconut tree.
On its trunk was a notice.
It said: 'DON'T DANCE!'

DON'T DANCE!

Zebra came and saw it.
  'Why ever not?' she said.
'I'll dance if I like.'
And she did.
  Bump! A coconut fell on her head.

'Ouch!' cried Zebra. 'There must be something up the coconut tree. I'll go and tell the king!'
And off she galloped.

Not far away from the river was another coconut tree. On its trunk was a notice. It said: 'DON'T CRY!'

Crocodile came and saw it.
'That's ridiculous,' he said.
'I'll cry if I like.'
And he did.

DON'T CRY!

Bump! A coconut fell on his head.

'Ouch!' cried Crocodile. 'There must be something up the coconut tree. I'll go and tell the king!' And off he scuttled.

Lion was having a snooze when
Ostrich, Zebra and Crocodile came
running to see him.

'Sire, Sire! Wake up!' they panted. 'There's something strange going on!' And they told him what had happened.

Lion was having a snooze when
Ostrich, Zebra and Crocodile came
running to see him.

'Sire, Sire! Wake up!' they panted. 'There's something strange going on!' And they told him what had happened.

Lion was not pleased at being disturbed. But he yawned and said, 'Mmm, it is rather strange. Let us go and find out about this.' And off they marched.

Somewhere in the jungle
was a coconut tree.
On its trunk was a notice.
It said: 'DON'T SING!'
Hippo came and saw it.
'What utter nonsense,'
she said. 'I'll sing
if I like.' And she did.
Bump! A coconut
fell on her head.

'Ouch!' cried Hippo.
'There must be
something up the
coconut tree.
I'll go and tell the king!'
And off she waddled.

Nearby, on a
patch of dry sand,
was another
coconut tree.
On its trunk was a
notice. It said:
'DON'T DO THE SPLITS!'

DON'T DO THE SPLITS!

Giraffe came and saw it.
'Who's going to stop me?'
she said. 'I'll do the splits
if I like.' And she did.
Bump! A coconut
fell on her head.

'Ouch!' cried Giraffe. 'There must be something up the coconut tree. I'll go and tell the king!' And off she loped.

Not far away from the edge of the bush was another coconut tree. On its trunk was a notice. It said: 'DON'T BLOW RASPBERRIES!'

Elephant came
and saw it.

DON'T BLOW
RASPBERRIES!

'Pah,' he said. 'I'll blow raspberries
if I like.' And he did.

Bump! A coconut fell on his head.

'Ouch!' cried Elephant. 'There must be something
up the coconut tree. I'll go and tell the king!'
And off he lumbered.

Soon Hippo, Giraffe and Elephant met
Lion, Ostrich, Zebra and Crocodile.
  'Sire, Sire!' they panted. 'There's something strange
going on!' And they told him what had happened.

'Mmm, it *is* strange,' said Lion, scratching his head.
'This must be dealt with at once. Come on!'
And off he went, leading the procession.

Somewhere in the jungle was a coconut tree. On its trunk
was a notice. It said: 'DON'T ROAR!'

Lion – followed by Ostrich, Zebra, Crocodile, Hippo, Giraffe and Elephant – came and saw it.

'Oh yes?' said Lion. 'We'll see about that.' And he let out a mighty, terrible, thunderous roar:

AAAAAAAARRRRRRRGGGGGGGGHHHHHHHH!
Bump! bump! bump! bump! bump! … !
A dozen coconuts fell on his head.

THUD – and a monkey!